HI, I'M CHLOE!

HI, I'M CHRIS!

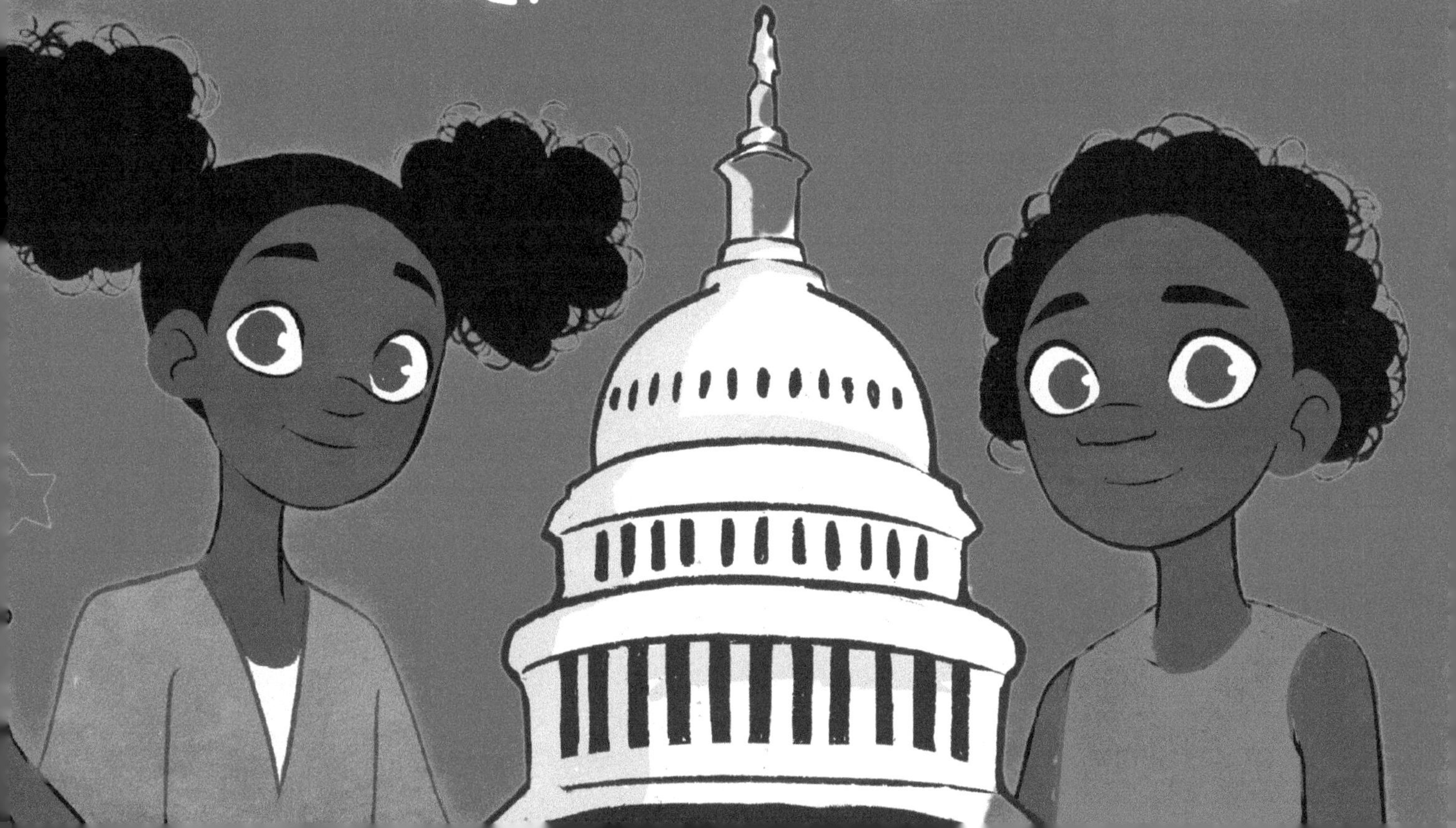

The Adventures of Chloe And Chris

The Three Branches of Government
Copyright © 2022 Magnolia Belle, LLC

Paperback ISBN: 978-1-7378345-6-4
Hardcover ISBN: 978-1-7378345-7-1

Editor: Crystal S. Wright

10 9 8 7 6 5 4 3 2
Printed in the United States

PRICELESS
PUBLISHING

Priceless Publishing®
pricelesspublishing.co
Lauderhill, Florida

DEDICATION

I dedicate this book to young readers and their families across the world. As you learn, explore, and gain awareness, you will have a positive imprint in your world. Continue to grow and shine your light.

ON THIS ADVENTURE YOU'LL LEARN ABOUT

The Three Branches of Government:

The Legislative Branch
The Executive Branch
The Judicial Branch

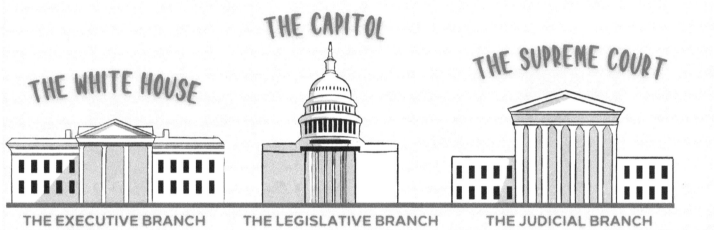

THE CAPITOL

THE WHITE HOUSE

THE SUPREME COURT

THE EXECUTIVE BRANCH   THE LEGISLATIVE BRANCH   THE JUDICIAL BRANCH

Chloe and Chris were playing in the park.
The yellow sun was setting. It was starting to get dark.

They were balanced on a seesaw when their mother said,
"Okay, let's go, you know the rules! It's almost time for bed."

"Your bedtime is at 8 and Chris's 8:30," she said to Chloe. But Chloe didn't like those rules, so she called out in a hurry.

How come I can't go to bed as late as my big brother?
Dad said, "Because you're younger."

Chloe wasn't having it. She did not like bedtime rules!
So she said, "If I were president I'd sleep whenever I choose.
I would sleep at 9, or maybe 10! Oh, how I wish it could be true.
I could boss around my brother because that's what presidents do."

Presidents make all the rules,
and that's how we get laws.
I would make a law that says
all bedtimes are on pause!

As president what I say goes,
and that's how it should be.
I would have ALL the power!
Imagine, President Me!

Mom said, "Actually, that's not exactly true.
If you were president, my dear,
that's not what you would do."

You'd be one part of government,
but just one of three:
Legislative, Executive, Judicial —
one, two, three.

"Three parts of government?" asked Chloe as curiosity took hold!
"So presidents, like me, have to do as they are told?
So presidents alone do not get all the perks?
I don't really get it! How does our government work?"

The Legislative Branch is the one that makes the laws. We also call it Congress. It's interesting because Congress is divided into two parts. One is called the Senate, and here's what senators do.

They are chosen by the people
to represent each state.
There are fifty states, and
each gets two: one hundred
is what that makes.

One hundred senators total, and
they're in office for six years.
When the people speak,
a good senator hears.

And remember I told you that Congress has two sides?
The House of Representatives is the other one that decides.

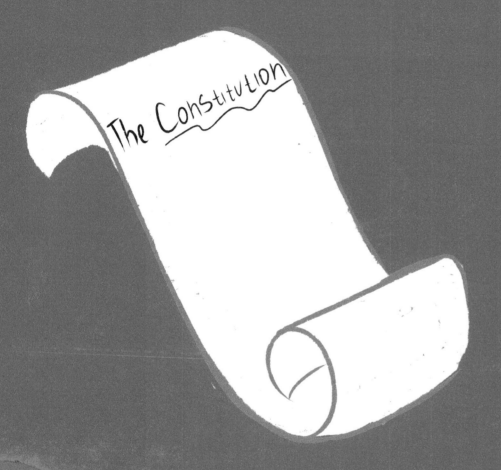

We vote for new ones every two years —
that's how we keep things fair.
That's how the House of Representatives
always has members who will care.

All of Congress goes to work in the Capitol, in DC. It's a great, big building with a large, white dome – quite a sight to see!

"But what about the President?" asked Chris.
"That big Capitol building,
is that where the President is?"

"Nope," their father said.
"The President lives close by,
In a place we call the White House,
when you see it you'll know why."

It's big and painted white, with a flag that sits on top. The President lives and works there all around the clock.

That's the second part of government,
called the Executive Branch.
There's lots of work to do there,
it's like an avalanche!

Every four years we elect
a new executive team.
See? Being a president isn't
exactly what it seems.

"And the last branch, is the Judicial Branch," said Mom. "Their job is to judge all the laws under the sun."

Is this law fair? Is that law good?
It's up to them to see.
Nine judges total to decide
which laws should be.

It's important to choose wisely, because once they decide, these nine judges keep their jobs for their entire lives!

The nine judges, or justices as they're called, work at the Supreme Court with their portraits on the walls.

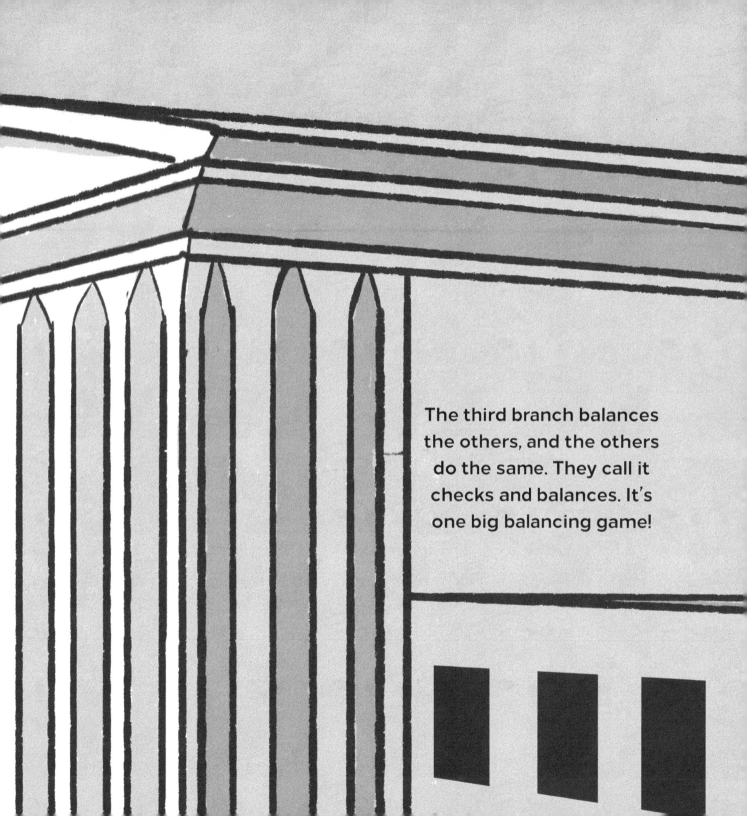

The third branch balances the others, and the others do the same. They call it checks and balances. It's one big balancing game!

The Supreme Court, the Capitol and the White House are all in DC. Someday we might visit, so that you can get to see.

Remember a senator gets six years, just to help review. While the President gets four years, and the representatives get two.

Brushing their teeth with toothpaste, making a lot of white foam.

They had learned much about government, and based on what was said, Chloe decided she was ready to go to bed.

"I think it's fair my bedtime is at 8," she finally declared.
"Balance is important, based on what you shared.
If I don't go to bed, tomorrow I'll be tired.
Maybe for my age, this bedtime is what's required."

Is this law fair? Is that law good?
It's up to them to see.
Nine judges total to decide
which laws should be.

It's important to choose wisely, because once they decide, these nine judges keep their jobs for their entire lives!

The nine judges, or justices as they're called, work at the Supreme Court with their portraits on the walls.

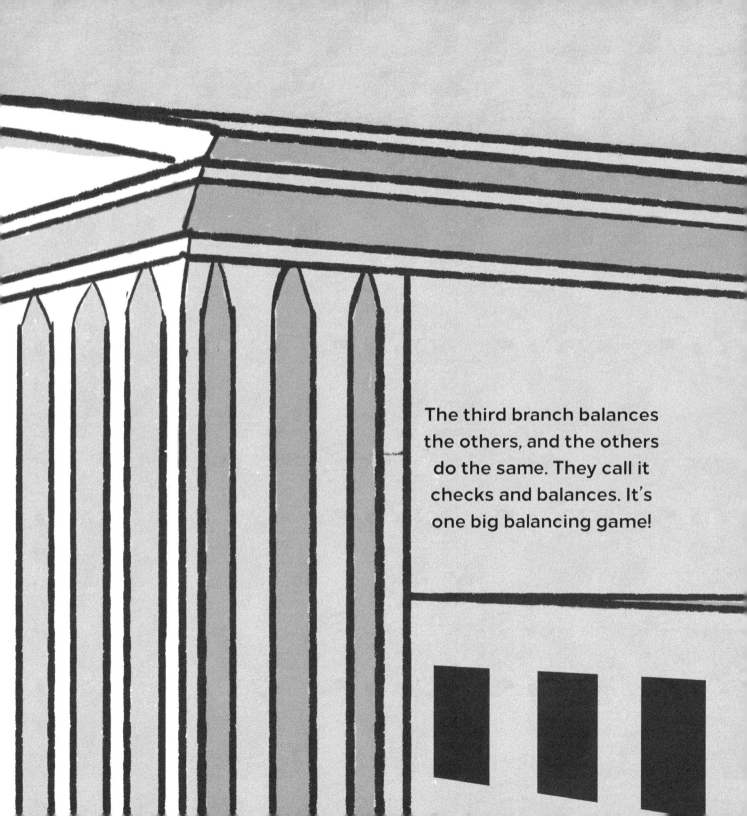

The third branch balances the others, and the others do the same. They call it checks and balances. It's one big balancing game!

The Supreme Court, the Capitol and the White House are all in DC. Someday we might visit, so that you can get to see.

Remember a senator gets six years, just to help review. While the President gets four years, and the representatives get two.

Brushing their teeth with toothpaste, making a lot of white foam.

They had learned much about government, and based on what was said, Chloe decided she was ready to go to bed.

"I think it's fair my bedtime is at 8," she finally declared.
"Balance is important, based on what you shared.
If I don't go to bed, tomorrow I'll be tired.
Maybe for my age, this bedtime is what's required."

How old do I have to be to be the President?
"Thirty-five — you still have time to spend," Dad said.
"That's old! I'll spend the time preparing," said Chris.
"Enforcing laws is the President's job, it's not just fame and glory."

"You can visit me at the White House," Chloe told Chris.
Chris responded, "Thanks for the invitation, sis!
Do you think that I could be your Vice President?
I'll help make people respect the laws 100 percent."

"Okay, let's shake on it," Chloe said and then she went to bed.
Her dreams were filled with images she had inside her head.

The White House, The Capitol, and The Supreme Court too —
all balanced, like a seesaw, with lots of things to do.

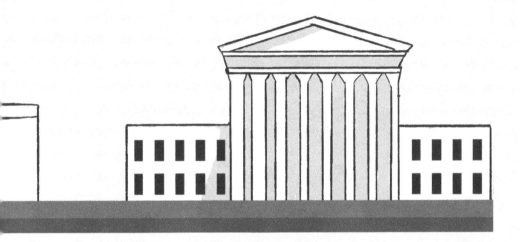

To make the laws, enforce them, and judge them right...
Chris had special dreams of his own that night.

Would you like to one day travel to DC?
Our government in action is
quite a sight to see!

ABOUT THE AUTHOR

HOPE E. GOINS is one of the most senior level staffers in the United States Congress. With over 15 years of experience in public service, she is responsible for advancing policy and legislation with Congressional leadership. Hope shares her unique experiences globally through her writing, keynote speeches, and panel discussions. She is a graduate of the Tougaloo College and the University of Arkansas School of Law.

STAY CONNECTED

Follow @THEADVENTURESOFCHLOEANDCHRIS on Instagram for continued American civics education featuring African American children.

For bulk orders of this book email ORDERS@THEADVENTURESOFCHLOEANDCHRIS.COM

CPSIA information can be obtained
at www.ICGtesting.com
Printed in the USA
JSHW052018301022
32351JS00001B/1